Table of Contents

Introduction to Geometric Tolerancing

Geometric Dimensioning and Tolerancing (GeoTol) is an international engineering language that is used on engineering drawings. It establishes a Cartesian coordinate system, also know as the datum reference frame, on the part. GeoTol uses a series of internationally recognized symbols to control the form, orientation and location of features on a part. These symbols applied through feature control frames are applied to the features and provide a clear definition of design intent. These principles are defined in the ASME Y14.5-2009 standard.

The ASME Y14.5.1-1994 (R2004) standard provides a mathematical interpretation of Dimensioning and Tolerancing.. The ASME Y14.5.2-2000 provides certification of Geometric Dimensioning and Tolerancing Professionals.

There are also international standards on geometric dimensioning and tolerancing, The introductory document being ISO 1101-2004. ISO (the International Organization for Standardization). It is a world-wide federation of national standards institutes (ISO member bodies). ASME is a source for American National Standards and international standards. See www.asme.org.

Drawings in this book contain a combination of both metric and inch values, recognizing the fact that both units are common within industry. Inch or Metric can be used without prejudice to the geometric tolerancing concepts illustrated in this text.

Note: The information in this text is based on ASME and ISO standards and though deemed to be correct must be considered as advisory and to be used at the discretion of the user. In some instances, figures show added detail for emphasis. In other cases, figures are incomplete by intent. Numerical values of dimensions and tolerances are illustrative only. Most examples in the text are in metric but the inch system can be used as well without prejudice. Be sure to consult national and international standards for more information on the subject. See also GeoTol Pro book for additional detailed information. **www.geotol.com**

ASME Standards- Product Definition and Metrology

The following is a reference list of American National Standards and ISO Standards that are related to geometric tolerancing, product definition, metrology and verification. These are some of the most common standards. Standards are in constant flux and change periodically. For more detailed information on current available standards contact:

The American Society of Mechanical Engineers (ASME)
www.ASME.Org
ISO Standards www.ds.dk/isotc213/

ASME Reference Standards

ASME Y14.5.1M-1994 (R2004), Mathematical Definition of Dimensioning and Tolerancing Principles

ASME Y14.5.2-2000 Certification of Geometric Dimensioning and Tolerancing Professionals

ASME Y14.41 - 2003 (R2008) Digital Product Definition Data Practices

ASME Y14.43 - 2003, (R2008) Dimensioning and Tolerancing Principles for Gages and Fixtures

ASME Y14.8-2009, Castings and Forgings

ANSI B4.2-1978 (R2004), Preferred Metric Limits and Fit

ANSI B4.1-1967 Preferred Limits and Fits for Cylindrical Parts

ASME Y13.38M-2007, Abbreviations

ASME Y14.100-2004, Engineering Drawing Practices

ASME Y14.3M-1994 (R2008), Multiview and Sectional View Drawings

ASME Y14.1M-2005, Drawing Sheet Size and Format

ASME Y14.2M-2008, Line Conventions and Lettering

ANSI/IEEE 268-1992,2 Metric Practice

IEEE/ASTM SI 10-2002 ERRATA 2005, Standard for Use of the International System of Units (SI) — The Modern Metric System

Fundamental Rules

Dimensioning and tolerancing shall clearly define engineering intent and conform to the following fundamental rules. See ASME Y14.5-2009 for additional information.

1. Each dimension shall have a tolerance, unless specifically identified as reference, maximum, minimum, or stock. (commercial stock size). The tolerance may be applied directly to the dimension (or indirectly in the case of basic dimensions) or indicated by a general note in the title block.

2. Dimensioning and tolerancing shall be complete so there is full understanding of the characteristics of each feature. Values may be expressed in an engineering drawing or in a CAD product definition data set.

3. Dimensions and tolerances shall be selected and arranged to suit the function and mating relationship of a part and shall not be subject to more than one interpretation. Each necessary dimension of an end product shall be shown in true profile views and refer to visible outlines. No more dimensions than those necessary for complete definition shall be given. The use of reference dimensions on a drawing should be minimized.

4. The drawing should define a part without specifying manufacturing methods. Thus, only the diameter of a hole is given without indicating whether it is to be drilled, reamed, punched, or made by any other operation. However, in those instances where manufacturing, processing, quality assurance, or environmental information is essential to the definition of engineering requirements, it shall be specified on the drawing or in a document referenced on the drawing.

5. A 90° angle with tolerance applies where center lines and lines depicting features are shown on a 2D orthographic drawing when defined by directly toleranced dimensions at right angles and no angle is specified.

Fundamental Rules (continued)

6. A 90° basic angle applies where center lines of features or surfaces shown at right angles on a 2D orthographic drawing when defined by basic dimensions and no angle is specified.

7. A zero basic dimension applies where axes, center planes, or surfaces are shown coincident on a drawing, and geometric tolerances establish the relationship among the features.

8. Unless otherwise specified, all dimensions and tolerances are applicable at 20°C (68°F) in accordance with ANSI/ASME B89.6.2.

9. Unless otherwise specified, all dimensions and tolerances apply in a free-state condition.

10. Unless otherwise specified, all tolerances apply for full depth, length, and width of the feature.

11. Dimensions and tolerances apply only at the drawing level where they are specified. A dimension specified for a given feature on one level of drawing (e.g., a detail drawing) is not mandatory for that feature at any other level (e.g., an assembly drawing).

12. Where a coordinate system is shown on the drawing, it shall be right-handed unless otherwise specified. Each axis shall be labeled and the positive direction shall be shown.

See GeoTol Pro Book for additional information. www.geotol.com

Common Symbols

This is a list of the most common symbols that are used on the face of a drawing. Note the comparison with the ISO standards. The symbols are used to replace text on the drawing and provide clear communication of design intent. The symbols marked with an "X" indicate new or revised from the previous ASME Y14.5M-1994 (R2004) standard.

	Term	Symbol ASME Y14.5	Symbol ISO
	Basic Dimension Theoretically Exact Dimension (ISO)	12	12
	Diameter	∅	∅
	Spherical Diameter	S∅	S∅
	Radius	R	R
	Controlled Radius	CR	None
	Spherical Radius	SR	SR
	Square	□	□
	Statistical Tolerance	⟨ST⟩	⟨ST⟩
	Reference Dimension	(12)	(12)
	Number of Places	3X	3X
	Counterbore	⌴	None
X	Spotface	⌴SF⌴	None
	Countersink	⌵	None
	Deep/Depth	⬇	None
	Envelope Principle	None	Ⓔ
X	Independency Principle	Ⓘ	None
	Dimension not to Scale	23	23
	Arc Length	⌢23	⌢23
	Slope	◺	◺
	Conical Taper	▷	▷
X	Continuous Feature	⟨CF⟩	None
	Dimension Origin	⬦→	⬦→
	First Angle Projection	⊟⊕	⊟⊕
	Third Angle Projection	⊕⊟	⊕⊟

6

Common Symbol Application

The drawing below is shown with many of the common symbols applied. The symbols are a universal method of specifying requirements without the use of notes or words.

Repetitive features such as holes, slots and tabs, which are repeated often, are specified by stating the number of features or places and an "X" and then followed by the requirement. The symbol for diameter is a circle with a slash. The symbol for radius is the letter R. The symbol for square features is a square box.

The symbol for counterbore and spot face are similar, except the spotface symbol will also have the letters SF inserted in the symbol. The countersink symbol is shown as a 90° Vee. The deep or depth symbol will identify the depth of the indicated feature.

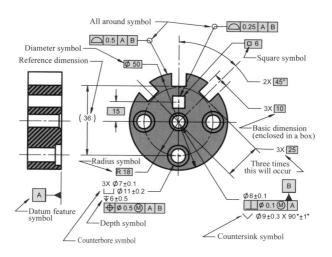

Symbols Associated with a Feature Control Frame

This table lists symbols that are commonly found in or associated with a feature control frame. The symbols marked with an "X" are new or revised from the previous ASME Y14.5M-1994 standard.

	TERM	SYMBOL ASME Y14.5	SYMBOL ISO
X	At Maximum Material Condition (MMC) (When applied to a feature) At Maximum Material Boundary (MMB) (When applied to a datum feature)	Ⓜ	Ⓜ
X	At Least Material Condition (LMC) (When applied to a feature) At Least Material Boundary (LMB) (When applied to a datum feature)	Ⓛ	Ⓛ
X	Regardless of Feature Size (RFS) (When applied to a feature) Regardless of Material Boundary (RMB) (When applied to a datum feature)	None Implied for features and datum features	None Implied for features and datum features
	Diameter	⌀	⌀
	Spherical Diameter	S⌀	S⌀
	Square	□	□
	Projected Tolerance Zone	Ⓟ	Ⓟ
	Free State	Ⓕ	Ⓕ
	Tangent Plane	Ⓣ	None
X	Translation	▷	None
X	Unequally Disposed Tolerance	Ⓤ	UZ (Proposed)
	Statistical Tolerance	⟨ST⟩	None
	All Around	⌀ (all around symbol)	⌀ (all around symbol)
X	All Over	⌀ (all over symbol)	Proposed
	Between	↔	Proposed

Symbols Related To Datum Identification

This table identifies terms and symbols that are commonly associated with establishing datums from datum features. The datum feature symbol represents contacting the high points of the datum feature. The datum target symbols represent datum simulator contact points, lines or areas on the datum feature. The movable datum target symbol marked with an "X" is new for the ASME Y14.5-2009 standard.

TERM	SYMBOL ASME Y14.5	SYMBOL ISO
Datum Feature		
Datum Feature ANSI Y14.5M-1982 (former standard)	– A –	None
Datum Target	Ø10 / A1	Ø10 / A1
Datum Target Point	A1	A1
Datum Target Line	A1	A1
Datum Target Area	Ø20 / A1	Ø20 / A1
X Movable Datum Target	A1	Proposed
Dimension Origin		

9

Features of size and Features without Size

Geometric tolerancing is a feature based system. A feature is a general term applied to a physical portion of a part such as a surface, pin, tab, hole or slot. Parts are composed of many features and are controlled with a feature control frame.

There are two types of features: Features of size and features without size. This is an important distinction in geometric tolerancing. Features of size can have feature modifiers such as MMC, LMC and RFS applied. Features without size can not have feature modifiers applied.

Examples of features without size: (Surfaces)

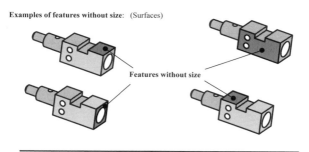

Features without size

Examples of features of size

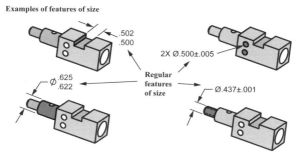

.502
.500

2X Ø.500±.005

Ø .625
.622

Regular features of size

Ø.437±.001

Material Conditions - MMC and LMC

These material condition modifiers are used in a feature control frame in the feature tolerance compartment and follow the feature tolerance. They are applicable when referring to features of size such as holes, slots, tabs, pins, etc. The application of the MMC and LMC modifiers provide additional geometric tolerance beyond the specified tolerance as the features depart from the specified condition. See unit 3 later in the text for the details.

Maximum Material Condition- Acronym - MMC
The condition where the feature contains the maximum material within the stated limits of size- for example, the largest pin or the smallest hole.
Least Material Condition - Acronym - LMC
The condition where the feature contains the least material within the stated limits of size- for example, the smallest pin or largest hole.

The drawing below identifies the MMC and LMC for each feature of size.

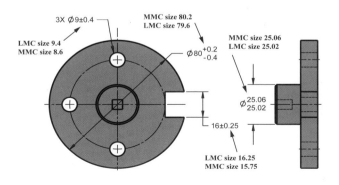

Geometric Tolerancing Characteristics

There are 14 geometric tolerancing characteristics. These characteristic symbols are placed in the first compartment of a feature control frame. They define the type of tolerance that is to be applied to the feature.

SYMBOL	GEOMETRIC CHARACTERISTIC	TYPE OF TOLERANCE	PRIMARY CONTROL
▱	FLATNESS	Form No relation between features	Controls form (shape) of surfaces and can also control form of an axis or median plane Datum reference is not allowed
—	STRAIGHTNESS		
⌭	CYLINDRICITY		
○	CIRCULARITY (ROUNDNESS)		
⊥	PERPENDICULARITY	Orientation No relation between features	Controls orientation (tilt) of surfaces, axes, or median planes for size and non-size features Datum reference required *Optional: Angularity symbol may be used for all orientation controls*
//	PARALLELISM		
∠	ANGULARITY		
⊕	POSITION	Location	Locates center points, axes and median planes for size features. Can also control orientation.
⌓	PROFILE OF A SURFACE		Locates surfaces Can also be used to control size, form, and orientation of surfaces based on datum reference
⌒	PROFILE OF A LINE		
⟰	TOTAL RUNOUT	Runout	Controls surface coaxiality Can also control form and orientation of surfaces.
↗	CIRCULAR RUNOUT		
◎	CONCENTRICITY	Location Derived median points.	Locates derived median points of a feature *Not common, consider position, runout, or profile.*
⊜	SYMMETRY		

Geometric Tolerance Categories

Form tolerances control the "shape" of features and are often used as a refinement of size.

Orientation tolerances control the "tilt" of features and are always associated with basic angle dimensions, often used as a refinement to location. If applied to surfaces, orientation tolerances also control form.

Location tolerances control location are always associated with basic linear dimensions. Position locates and orients the median plane or axis of features of size. Profile locates feature surfaces and can also also control orientation, form and size.

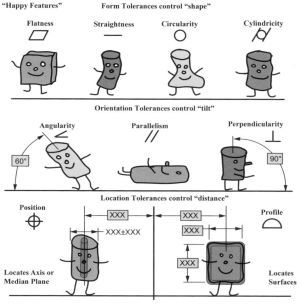

"Happy Features"   **Form Tolerances control "shape"**

Flatness   Straightness   Circularity   Cylindricity

Orientation Tolerances control "tilt"

Angularity   Parallelism   Perpendicularity
60°   90°

Location Tolerances control "distance"

Position   Profile
XXX   XXX
XXX±XXX   XXX
XXX

Locates Axis or Median Plane   Locates Surfaces

Common Tolerance Zone Shapes

Geometric tolerancing is a three dimensional language. A datum reference frame (Cartesian coordinate system) is established on a part. Geometric tolerancing is applied to the part features. The applied geometric specifications create zones of tolerance within which the feature must lie.

The shapes shown above are the most common shaped tolerance zones. The zones are parallel planes, squares, cylinders, uniform boundaries etc.

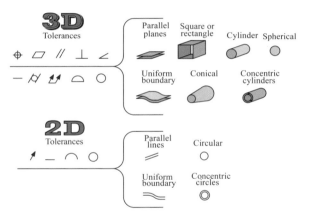

The engineer can also create jelly bean zones, amoeba shaped zones or just about any shape desired. The use of geometric tolerancing can be simple or complex, depending on the necessary requirements. The Geometric tolerancing system is a very powerful language and can be used to define the most complex design criteria for the most discriminating situations.

Feature Control Frame

The feature control frame states the requirements or instructions for the feature to which it is attached. As its name implies, the feature control frame controls features. Each feature control frame will state only one requirement or one message. There is only one set up or one requirement for each feature control frame. If it is necessary to have two requirements for a feature, it requires two feature control frames.

The feature controlled can be a surface or a feature of size, like a hole shown in the example below. If the feature has size, the size requirements for the feature will be defined.

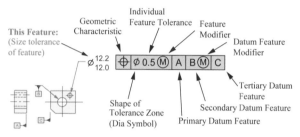

The first compartment of a feature control frame contains one of the 14 geometric characteristic symbols. The geometric characteristic symbol will specify the requirement for the feature such as: This feature must be flat, or this feature must be positioned, etc.

The second compartment of a feature control frame contains the total tolerance for the feature. The feature tolerance is always a total tolerance. It is never a plus/minus value.

If the tolerance is preceded by a diameter symbol (Ø), the tolerance is a diameter or cylindrical shaped zone, as in the position of a hole. If there is no symbol preceding the tolerance, the default tolerance zone shape is parallel planes or a total wide zone.

Following the feature tolerance in the feature control frame, a material condition modifier such as MMC or LMC may be specified if the feature has size, such as for a hole, slot, tab, pin etc. If the feature has size and no modifier is specified, the default modifier is RFS. If the feature has no size, such as a plane surface, then a feature modifier is not applicable.

The third and following compartments of the feature control frame contain the specified datum feature reference(s) if datum references are required. The alphabetical order of the datum references has no significance. The significance is their order of precedence reading from left to right as primary, secondary and tertiary. See GeoTol Pro book for more information.

Basic Dimensions

Basic dimensions are theoretically exact numerical values or mathematical expressions used to define the form, size, orientation or location of a part or feature. Basic dimensions are enclosed in a box. They may also be invoked by a note on the drawing or by referencing a standard that contains these requirements.

The mathematical data set in a CAD model may also be defined as basic. Permissible variations from basic dimensions are usually defined in a feature control frame or by other notes on a drawing. **The default ± tolerances stated in the title block of a drawing do not apply to basic dimensions.**

Index Plate - Practical Example

The establishment of a Datum Reference Frame (DRF) and the application of geometric tolerances are applied to parts based on functional design requirements. An index assembly is shown below. The top index plate clamps on its face and is centered by the pilot pin. The plate is rotationally aligned in the assembly with the side planar surface. The index plate is then bolted down in the assembly with three screws.

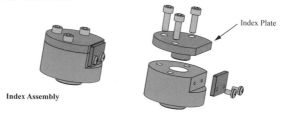

Index Plate

Index Assembly

The engineering drawing below reflects geometric tolerance applied to the index plate based on functional assembly conditions. The A, B, C, datum reference frame is established and qualified from features on the part based on functional mating conditions. The primary datum feature A, is the large planar face; its form is qualified with a flatness specification. The secondary datum feature B is the OD of the pilot, and it is oriented with a perpendicularity specification with respect to datum A.

The tertiary datum feature planar surface, is located with respect to the A,B - DRF with a profile specification. The remaining features on the part are located with respect to the A,B,C - DRF with position and profile tolerances that are appropriate to their importance in the assembly. The outside surface of the part is located with a relatively large profile tolerance. The 3 holes have more restrictive position tolerances applied.

Engineering drawing with applied geometric tolerancing based on functional requirements

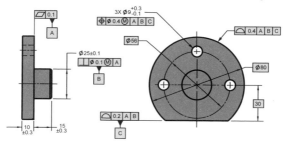

Index Plate - Perfect DRF to an Imperfect Part

The produced index plate has imperfect geometry because of variation in manufacturing. This illustration shows how the theoretical perfect geometry of the design A, B, C - DRF is mated to the imperfect geometry of the produced part. The geometry, sequence of events and corresponding terminology in the mating process are the basics to understand geometric tolerancing and are used throughout this text. Detailed definitions of these terms can be found in the GeoTol Pro book and in the ASME Y14.5-2009 standard. All dimensions originate from the Datum Reference Frame (DRF) and not the part.

Establishment of A, B, C - DRF on the produced index plate.

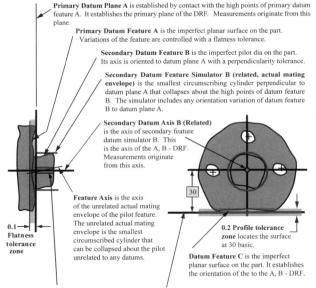

Primary Datum Plane A is established by contact with the high points of primary datum feature A. It establishes the primary plane of the DRF. Measurements originate from this plane.

Primary Datum Feature A is the imperfect planar surface on the part. Variations of the feature are controlled with a flatness tolerance.

Secondary Datum Feature B is the imperfect pilot dia on the part. Its axis is oriented to datum plane A with a perpendicularity tolerance.

Secondary Datum Feature Simulator B (related, actual mating envelope) is the smallest circumscribing cylinder perpendicular to datum plane A that collapses about the high points of datum feature B. The simulator includes any orientation variation of datum feature B to datum plane A.

Secondary Datum Axis B (Related) is the axis of secondary feature datum simulator B. This is the axis of the A, B - DRF. Measurements originate from this axis.

Feature Axis is the axis of the unrelated actual mating envelope of the pilot feature. The unrelated actual mating envelope is the smallest circumscribed cylinder that can be collapsed about the pilot unrelated to any datums.

0.1 ⟷
Flatness tolerance zone

30

0.2 Profile tolerance zone locates the surface at 30 basic.

Datum Feature C is the imperfect planar surface on the part. It establishes the orientation of the to the A, B - DRF.

Orientation Tolerance Zone is a 0.1 cylindrical tolerance zone that is perpendicular to datum plane A. The unrelated feature axis of the pilot must fall within this zone.

Tertiary Datum Plane C is established from a datum feature simulator (Related) perfect plane that is oriented 90° to datum plane A, relative to datum axis B and progresses toward tertiary datum feature C to make maximum possible contact with the high points on the datum feature. This plane sets the orientation planes of the DRF.

Index Plate - Practical Example in 3D

3D Model Tolerancing

This is an example of geometric tolerancing applied to the solid model based on the functional requirements of the assembly. An A,B,C - DRF is established and qualified. All untoleranced dimensions are basic and can be found in the CAD math data. The remaining features on the part are located to the DRF. Features on the model can also be queried for specifications.

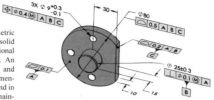

See digital data file 2324 for hole and surface locations.

The drawing above is an example of geometric tolerancing applied to a solid model. This drawing is per the ASME Y14.41-2003 (R2008) standard. This standard shows how to symbolically apply geometric tolerancing to the digital model, but does not replace the ASME Y14.5 standard, it just allows and extends the geometric tolerancing principles to digital models. For definitions and technical definitions of geometric tolerancing principles, the ASME Y14.5-2009 standard is the primary document.

Notice on the drawing above that many dimensions are not shown but can be found in the digital file. The digital file dimensions are basic. Geometric tolerances are applied to the features by the use of feature control frames. As you can see, it would be impossible to use directly toleranced or plus/minus type dimensions on this type of product definition. For this new technology, and the eventual goal of a paperless system to advance, it is critical to use geometric tolerancing. The GeoTol Pro book has additional information on the subject of geometric tolerancing. www.geotol.com

Limits of Size - Rule #1

The limits of size is an important concept that defines the size and form limits for an individual regular feature of size. In the ASME Y14.5, it is referred to as Rule #1 or the Envelope Principle.

A drawing of a pin and a hole are shown below along with a size dimension. The limits of size ensures the pin will fit in the hole by requiring perfect form at MMC. The extreme variations of size and form allowed on an individual, regular feature of size are shown below.

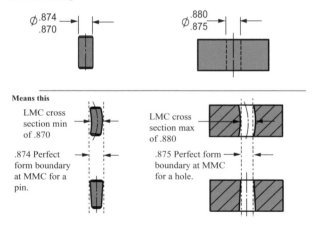

The limits of size define the size, as well as the form of an individual feature. The form of the feature may vary within the size limits. If the feature is produced at its maximum material condition, the form must be perfect. The feature may be bent, tapered or out of round as it departs from the maximum material condition.

No Implied Relationship Between Size Features

This on the drawing

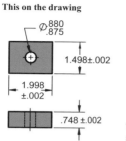

UNLESS OTHERWISE
SPECIFIED: ANGLES ± 1°

Allows measurements to be not square to each other

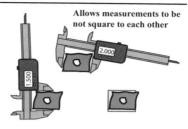

The ±1° angle tolerance between the features of size allows the part to be a parallelogram and may not fit in a 1.500 X 2.000 perfect rectangular box.

There is no implied relationship between the size toleranced features except the specified angle tolerance. Perfect form at MMC is for individual features, not the interrelationship between features.

This on the drawing

Establishes basic 90° angles that are square to the each other and datum feature A.

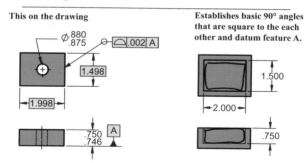

The drawing above has the surfaces related to each other by the basic linear dimensions and the unspecified, but implied basic 90° angles. The profile tolerance is applied all around and referenced to datum feature A. This will insure the part will fit in a 1.500 X 2.000 perfectly rectangular box. A profile tolerance will control the relationship between features.

21

Profile Replaces Plus/Minus for Location of Surfaces

Profile tolerance replaces the traditional plus/minus or direct type tolerancing for the location of surfaces. The two examples below illustrate a sheet metal part mounted in an assembly. Datums are selected based on functional mounting conditions.

This application

The short surface is identified as the datum feature and the long surface is located to the datum with a profile tolerance. The datum feature is qualified with a flatness tolerance.

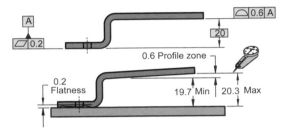

This application

The long surface is identified as the datum feature and the short surface is located to the datum with a profile tolerance. The datum feature is qualified with a flatness tolerance.

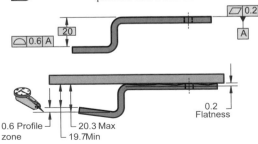

Effect of Regardless of Feature Size (RFS)

Since no modifier is specified the geometric tolerance is implied RFS. See modifier rules. The specified geometric tolerance is independent of the actual size of the feature. The allowable geometric tolerance is limited to the specified value in the feature control frame regardless of the actual size of the feature.

The feature control frame below states that the holes must be positioned within a 0.6 diameter tolerance zone. This requires the features to be positioned within a 0.6 diameter position zone regardless of the feature size. There is no additional position tolerance allowed as the holes get larger or smaller. The RFS condition is more restrictive than the MMC or LMC concept. See table.

Feature Ø Size	Ø Position Tol Allowed
11.7	0.6
11.8	0.6
11.9	0.6
12	0.6
12.1	0.6
12.2	0.6
12.3	0.6

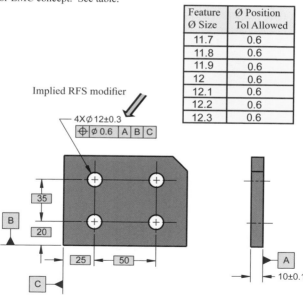

Effect of Maximum Material Condition (MMC) Modifier

The Maximum Material Condition (MMC) modifier is applied by placing the circle M symbol in the feature control frame following the feature tolerance. This provides the feature with additional geometric tolerance as the feature's size departs from its maximum material condition. The MMC modifier may only be applied to features of size MMC is not applicable to features without size.

The maximum material condition for the holes are 11.7 diameter. If the holes depart (get larger) from their maximum material condition size, they are allowed additional position tolerance equal to the amount of their departure from their MMC size of 11.7.

The MMC modifier in the feature control frame invokes the MMC concept and allows additional position tolerance as the features depart from their MMC. See table.

Feature Ø Size	Ø Position Tol Allowed
11.7	0.6
11.8	0.7
11.9	0.8
12	0.9
12.1	1
12.2	1.1
12.3	1.2

MMC modifier

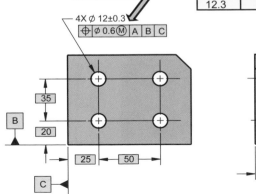

24

Effect of Zero Tolerancing at MMC

There are many cases where features of size may be controlled with a zero geometric tolerance. If a feature is specified with a zero geometric tolerance, it must be modified at MMC or LMC. The RFS concept is not applicable with a zero geometric tolerance.

The example below illustrates holes positioned with zero tolerance at MMC. The allowable position tolerance for the holes is dependent on the actual size of the holes. The MMC modifier in the feature control frame allows additional position tolerance equal in amount to the holes departure from their MMC size of 11.1. See table.

If properly applied zero tolerancing at MMC provides maximum position tolerance while still maintaining a full range of size tolerance.

Feature Ø Size	Ø Position Tol Allowed
11.1	0
11.2	0.1
11.3	0.2
11.4	0.3
11.5	0.4
11.6	0.5
11.7	0.6
11.8	0.7
11.9	0.8
12	0.9
12.1	1
12.2	1.1
12.3	1.2

MMC modifier

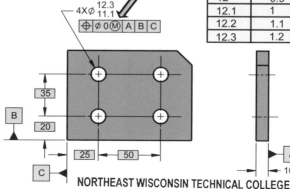

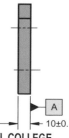

Effect of Least Material Condition (LMC) Modifier

The Least Material Condition (LMC) modifier is applied by placing the circle L symbol in the feature control frame following the feature tolerance. This provides the feature with additional geometric tolerance as the feature's size departs from its least material condition. The LMC modifier may only be applied to features of size LMC is not applicable to features without size.

The least material condition for the holes are 12.3 diameter. If the holes depart (get smaller) from their least material condition size, they are allowed additional position tolerance equal to the amount of their departure from their LMC size of 12.3.

The LMC modifier in the feature control frame invokes the LMC concept and allows additional position tolerance as the features depart from their LMC. See table.

Feature Ø Size	Ø Position Tol Allowed
12.3	0.6
12.2	0.7
12.1	0.8
12	0.9
11.9	1
11.8	1.1
11.7	1.2

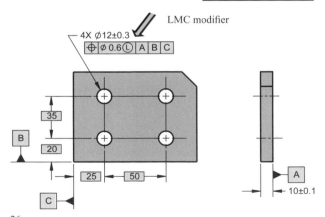

LMC modifier

26

Material condition modifiers are found in a feature control frame. They will have a different effect on the geometric specification depending on the modifier and how and where they are applied. There are two types of material condition modifiers, feature modifiers and datum feature modifiers.

$$\boxed{\oplus \; \varnothing \, 0.3 \, \text{\textcircled{M}} \; A \; D \, \text{\textcircled{M}} \; E \, \text{\textcircled{M}}}$$

Feature Modifiers ↗ ↖ **Datum Feature Modifiers**

Ⓜ Maximum Material Condition (MMC)   Ⓜ Maximum Material Boundary (MMB)

Ⓛ Least Material Condition (LMC)   Ⓛ Least Material Boundary (LMB)

Regardless of Feature Size (RFS)   Regardless of Material Boundary (RMB)
(Implied by default)   (Implied by default)

RFS and RMB apply by default for all geometric tolerances.

Regardless of Feature Size (RFS) applies by default, for all feature tolerances in a feature control frame where no modifying symbol is specified. Regardless of Material Boundary (RMB) applies by default for all datum feature references in a feature control frame where no modifier symbol is specified.

MMC, LMC, MMB and LMB must be specified to apply.

If required, the feature modifiers, Maximum Material Condition (MMC) and Least Material Condition (LMC) must be specified in the feature control frame. Likewise, if the datum feature modifiers, Maximum Material Boundary (MMB) and Least Material Boundary (LMB) are required, they must be specified in the feature control frame.

27

Modifier Rules - Former Practices

Former Practice ASME Y14.5M-1994 (R2004)

The ASME Y14.5M-1994 standard stated that RFS applied for all geometric tolerances and datum references.

If MMC or LMC are to apply for geometric tolerances or datum references, they must be specified.

Former Practice ANSI Y14.5M-1982

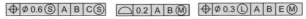

The ANSI Y14.5M-1982 standard stated that MMC, RFS and LMC must be specified when applying position tolerances for both feature tolerance and datum feature references.

RFS is implied for all feature tolerances and datum features on all other geometric tolerances. If MMC or LMC is required, it must be specified.

Former Practice ANSI Y14.5M-1973

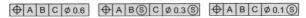

The ANSI Y14.5M-1973 standard stated that MMC was implied for position tolerances for both the feature tolerances and datum feature references. If LMC or RFS is required, it must be specified.

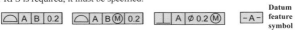

RFS is implied for all feature tolerances and datum features on all other geometric tolerances. If MMC or LMC is required, it must be specified. Notice the datum feature references preceed the tolerance in the ANSI Y14.5M-1973 standard.

General Rules - Screw Threads and Gears/Splines

Srew Thread Rule

A screw thread has three diameters, the major diameter, minor diameter and pitch diameter. The pitch diameter is usually the theoretical functional mating diameter. According to the ASME Y14.5-2009 standard, the pitch diameter applies by default to the geometric tolerance and/or the datum reference. Thread wires or a thread gage are often used to establish the axis in inspection.

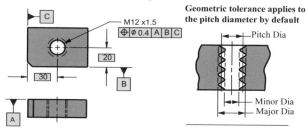

Geometric tolerance applies to the pitch diameter by default

If the major diameter or minor diameter is required to apply, it must be specified. The term MAJOR or MINOR diameter is stated under the feature control frame or under the datum feature symbol, as applicable. The adjacent example illustrates a position tolerance applied to the major diameter and a datum feature reference applied to the pitch diameter.

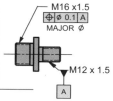

Gear and Spline Rule

A gear or spline is composed of a variety of diameters. According to the ASME Y14.5-2009 standard and ISO standard it must be specifically stated which diameter is desired. There is no default condition. The required diameter, MAJOR DIA, PITCH DIA, MINOR DIA is to be stated directly under the feature control frame.

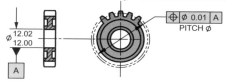

Virtual Condition

Depending on function, a feature may be controlled with a size tolerance and geometric control. The geometric control may also include an MMC modifier. Consideration must be given to the collective effects of MMC and applicable tolerances in determining the clearance between parts and in establishing gage feature sizes. When a MMC modifier is applied to the feature, it creates a constant virtual condition boundary in which the feature must be contained. This calculated boundary is used to find the worst case clearance for two parts fitting together.

Pins appear larger at virtual

To calculate virtual condition for external features, start with the largest feature and add the geometric tolerance.

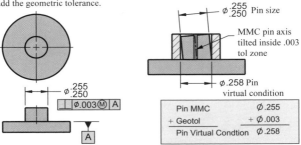

Pin MMC	ϕ.255
+ Geotol	+ ϕ.003
Pin Virtual Condtion	ϕ.258

Holes appear smaller at virtual

To calculate virtual size for internal features, start with the smallest feature and subtract the geometric tolerance.

Hole MMC	ϕ.265
- Geotol	- ϕ.003
Hole Virtual Condition	ϕ.262

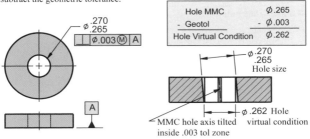

Virtual Condition - Multiple Controls

Virtual condition is a constant boundary generated by the collective effects of size and the geometric tolerance applied. Sometimes, features may have multiple geometric controls. This will create multiple virtual sizes. The pin below has a size tolerance and two feature control frames applied, and therefore two virtual size boundaries are created. The .255 diameter virtual size relative to datum A is a result of the perpendicularity tolerance. The .265 diameter virtual size relative to datums A, B, and C is a result of the position tolerance.

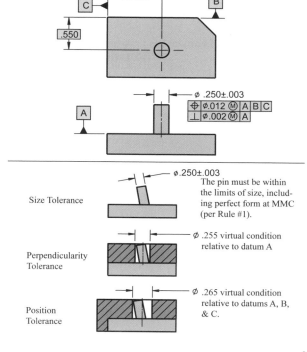

Size Tolerance

φ.250±.003
The pin must be within the limits of size, including perfect form at MMC (per Rule #1).

Perpendicularity Tolerance

φ .255 virtual condition relative to datum A

Position Tolerance

φ .265 virtual condition relative to datums A, B, & C.

31

A Datum Reference Frame Constrains 6 Degrees of Freedom

The Datum Reference Frame (DRF) consists of 3 planes, 3 axes that are mutually perpendicular and intersect at a point. The datum reference frame is the origin of all the dimensions and geometric specifications that are referenced to it.

The DRF is associated to the part and establishes 6 Degrees of Freedom (DOF), three translations and three rotations. The three translational degrees of freedom are termed X, Y and Z. The three rotational degrees of freedom are termed u (rotation about the X axis), v (rotation about the Y axis) and w (rotation about the Z axis).

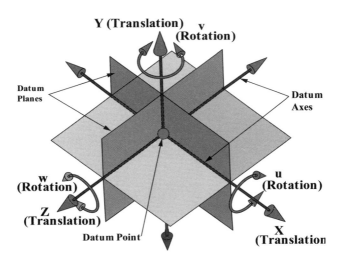

Three Translation Controls
X = Translation in "X" direction
Y = Translation in "Y" direction
Z = Translation in "Z" direction

Three Rotation Controls
u = Rotation in "u" direction
v = Rotation in "v" direction
w = Rotation in "w" direction

The **Datum Reference Frame (DRF)** in design engineering is a three dimensional, Cartesian coordinate system. The engineers work in this theoretically perfect coordinate system to mathematically define their product and make necessary calculations. Dimensions and tolerances originate from this DRF.

Mathematics
Cartesian coordinate system

CAD System

The DRF is established on the part by engaging the datum features with simulators and establishing datums in an order of precedence.

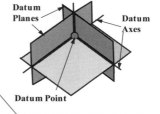

Datum Planes

Datum Axes

Datum Point

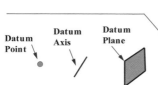

Datum Point

Datum Axis

Datum Plane

Datums are points, axes (lines), and planes or some combination of these components. They are established from theoretical datum feature simulators.

Theoretical datum feature simulator is the perfect inverse of a datum feature. (cylinders, widths etc.) They engage with datum features and establish datums. *Formerly called True Geometric Counterpart (TGC).*

Datum simulator

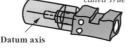

Datum axis

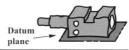

Datum plane

Datum features are the actual, physical features on the part. They are not perfect, they have variation.

Datum Feature References Apply in a Stated Order

The DRF is established iand mated to the part in an order, as stated from the datum features referenced in the rear compartments of the feature control frame. The primary datum feature is shown in the first compartment. In this case, it mates with the DRF on the highest 3 points of the surface. The secondary datum feature is mates next and the tertiary follows.

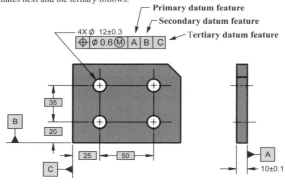

The order of the datum features in the rear compartment of the feature control frame mate the DRF to the part.

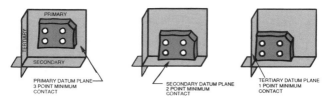

PRIMARY DATUM PLANE
3 POINT MINIMUM CONTACT

SECONDARY DATUM PLANE
2 POINT MINIMUM CONTACT

TERTIARY DATUM PLANE
1 POINT MINIMUM CONTACT

To achieve interchangeable parts, it is mandatory datum reference frame is established on parts. The DRF is a 3D coordinate system where all dimensions and measurements originate. If the DRF is not clear the product will not be well-defined, which leads to misunderstandings, confusion and poor quality. See GeoTol Book for additional informtaion on establishing datum reference frames.

Constraining Degrees of Freedom

Datum features referenced in a feature control frame establish a DRF based on an order of precedence. These datum features constrain the six degrees of freedom on a part. A lower precedence datum feature can not override, constrain or eliminate any datums or degrees of freedom already established by any higher precedence datum features. Each subsequent referenced datum feature in the feature control frame will constrain all the degrees of freedom that is possible within its ability.

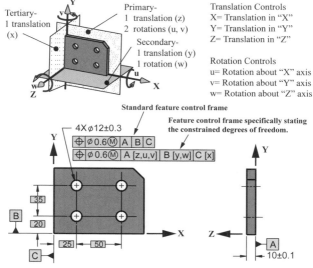

Translation Controls
X= Translation in "X"
Y= Translation in "Y"
Z= Translation in "Z"

Rotation Controls
u= Rotation about "X" axis
v= Rotation about "Y" axis
w= Rotation about "Z" axis

The lower feature control frame explicitly states the degrees of freedom constrained by each datum feature shown in the upper feature control frame. In a standard feature control frame it is not necessary to state the degrees of freedom constrained, as this default mating condition is clearly defined by the simulator requirements. This figure is only used as an example to show mathematically how the datum reference frame is created by the datum features in an established order of precedence. If it is necessary to override the default mating conditions then a customized datum reference frame can be used. See GeoTol Pro book for details.

35

This table lists datum features referenced as a primary datum feature at RMB. Any feature or combinations of features can become a datum feature. The degrees of freedom they constrain is dependent on their geometry. See GeoTol Pro book for more information.

Feature Type	On the Drawing	Datum Feature	Datum and Datum Feature Simulator	Datum and Constraining DOF
Planar (a)			Plane	1 Trans 2 Rotate
Width (b)			Plane	1 Trans 2 Rotate
Cylindrical (c)			Axis	2 Trans 2 Rotate
Spherical (d)			Point	3 Trans 0 Rotate
Conical (e)			Axis & Plane	3 Trans 2 Rotate
Linear Extrusion (f)			2 Planes	2 Trans 3 Rotate
Complex (g)			3 Planes	3 Trans 3 Rotate

Planar Datum Features- Datum Planes

Datum feature symbols applied to planar features establish a datum plane which contacts the high points of the surface. The datum feature symbol may be attached to the surface or to an extension line of a surface. or placed on a feature control frame that is attached to the extension line as shown with datum feature L. It can also be placed on a leader line that is directed to the surface or extension line as shown with datum feature N. If a datum plane is to be derived from multiple surfaces, the number of surfaces should be noted, as shown with datum feature K.

Planar datum features

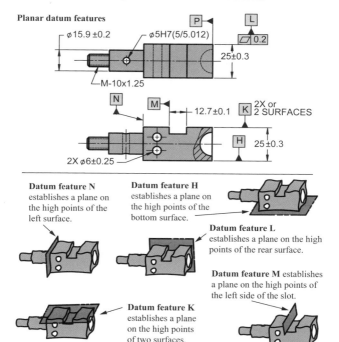

Datum feature N establishes a plane on the high points of the left surface.

Datum feature H establishes a plane on the high points of the bottom surface.

Datum feature L establishes a plane on the high points of the rear surface.

Datum feature M establishes a plane on the high points of the left side of the slot.

Datum feature K establishes a plane on the high points of two surfaces.

37

Datum Features with Size - Center Planes, Axes and Points

The detail drawing shows datum feature symbols applied to features of size that establish a datum axis, center plane or point. The datum feature symbol is never applied directly to the center line of a feature. The datum feature symbol is attached to, or associated with the size dimension of a feature. A datum feature simulator, which is the inverse of the feature, which is mated with the feature and the datum axis, center plane or point (or combination of), is then derived from the datum feature simulator.

Datum features of size

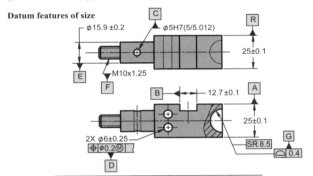

Establishing a datum axis from an external cylinder, datum feature E at RMB

Theory

Datum axis E is the axis of the theoretical datum feature simulator.

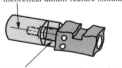

The cylindrical datum feature is mated with a theoretical datum feature simulator that is a circumscribing cylinder collapsing on the high points of the feature. The datum axis is the axis of the theoretical datum feature simulator.

Physical   Simulated datum axis E is the axis of a collet,

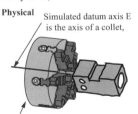

The cylindrical datum feature is mated with a physical datum feature simulator, like a collapsing collet. The simulated datum axis is the axis of the physical simulator or collet.

The Placement of Datum Feature Symbols is very Important

The placement of the datum feature symbol is very important. Datum features M and K are datum features without size and establish datum planes that are derived from the high points of the planar surface of the datum feature. The datum feature symbol is placed on the extension line of the feature, clearly removed from the size dimension line. Datum features B and R are datum features with size, and establish the center plane of the features as datums. The datum feature symbol is placed in line with the size dimension line.

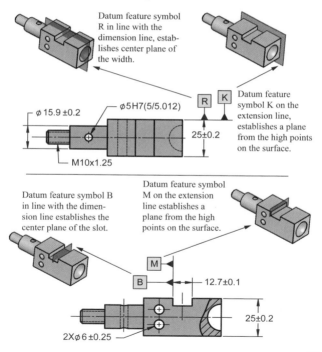

Datum feature symbol R in line with the dimension line, establishes center plane of the width.

Datum feature symbol K on the extension line, establishes a plane from the high points on the surface.

Datum feature symbol B in line with the dimension line establishes the center plane of the slot.

Datum feature symbol M on the extension line establishes a plane from the high points on the surface.

ø15.9 ±0.2

ø5H7(5/5.012)

25±0.2

M10x1.25

12.7±0.1

25±0.2

2Xø6 ±0.25

Partial Datum Features

If a feature or group of features are identified as a datum feature, the entire surface of the feature shall be used to establish the datum. In some cases, an engineer might find it desirable to identify only a portion of a surface as a datum feature. In these cases, a partial datum feature may be identified on the drawing. Examples of partial datum features are shown below. A leader line terminating with a dot within the outline of a surface can be used to identify a partial datum within the outline of a surface. If necessary, the partial area is identified with basic dimensions and may be cross-hatched for clarity. Datum targets are another method to establish partial datum features. See GeoTol Book for more information.

Partial datum featues

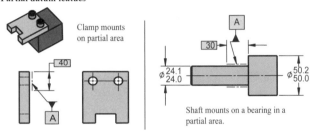

Shaft mounts on a bearing in a partial area.

The shaft mounts on two bearing surfaces simultaneously. The datum feature letters are entered in the primary compartment of the feature control frame, separated by a dash. Both datum features together establish a single primary datum axis.

Multiple datum featues

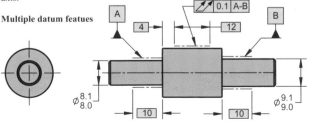

Establishing the N, E, H DRF on the Part

The sequence of events to establish the N, E, H datum reference frame to constrain the 6 degrees of freedom on the part.

⊕ |⌀0.4Ⓜ| N | E | H |

A lower precedence datum can not override the degrees of freedom already established by a previous datum. The qualification of the datum features with flatness, perpendicularity and profile are necessary to relate the imperfect datum features to the perfect DRF.

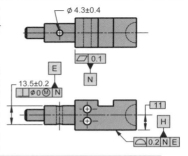

---

① ⊕ |⌀0.4Ⓜ| N |

Datum feature N is in the first compartment as the primary datum feature. It establishes a plane and constrains 1 translation and 2 rotations. The surface is qualified with a flatness tolerance.

3 point min contact to establish primary plane

② ⊕ |⌀0.4Ⓜ| N | E |

Datum feature E is in the second compartment as the secondary datum feature. It establishes an axis and constrains 2 translations. The intersection of the axis and plane establish a point. The feature is oriented with a perpendicularity tolerance.

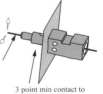

3 point min contact to establish secondary datum axis

---

③ ⊕ |⌀0.4Ⓜ| N | E | H |

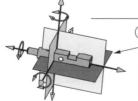

Datum feature H is entered in the third compartment as the tertiary datum feature. It establishes a plane and constrains 1 rotation. The datum feature is located relative to datums N and E with a profile tolerance. The DRF is complete and all 6 degrees of freedom are constrained on the part.

Datum Feature Simulator Requirements

Referencing datum features in an order of precedence in a feature control frame establishes a series of datum feature simulators. The size, form, orientation, location, growth or movement of these simulators are based on the datum feature modifier specified according to the datum feature simulator requirements shown below.

Datums are established from these datum feature simulators. These datums in their referenced order of precedence, establish the datum reference frame. The datum feature simulator requirements shown below are the foundation principles for establishing a DRF from datum features referenced in a feature control frame. These requirements are critical to understanding the development of datum reference frames shown in this pocket guide. See GeoTol book for more info.

Datum Feature Simulators

1. They shall have perfect form. They are perfectly round, cylindrical, straight, flat and with perfect geometry.

2. They have basic orientation relative to one another as referenced in a feature control frame. The orientation (tilt), like angularity, perpendicularity or parallelism, is perfect.

3. They have basic location relative to one another as referenced in a feature control frame, unless a translation modifier or moveable datum target symbol is specified.

4. They have movable location when the translation modifier or the movable datum target symbol is specified.

5. They expand, compress or otherwise progress in their order of precedence, to make maximum contact with the datum feature when specified at RMB.

6. They are fixed at the designated size, when specified at MMB or LMB.

A lower precedence datum feature can not override, constrain or eliminate any datums or degrees of freedom already established by any higher precedence datum feature(s). Each subsequent referenced datum feature in the feature control frame will constrain all the degrees of freedom that is possible within its ability.

Note: If it is necessary to override these foundational datum feature simulator requirements it may be accomplished with a customized datum reference frame explained in detail in GeoTol Pro book. **www.geotol.com**

Datum Feature Precedence and Modifiers

The order of datum features referenced in a feature control frame are based on functional assembly requirements as shown in the three examples shown below.

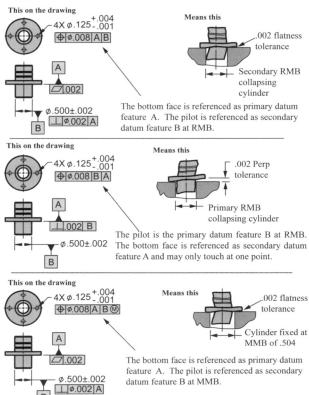

This on the drawing

4X ⌀.125 +.004/−.001
⊕ ⌀.008 A B

A
⬦ .002

⌀.500±.002
⊥ ⌀.002 A
B

Means this

.002 flatness tolerance

Secondary RMB collapsing cylinder

The bottom face is referenced as primary datum feature A. The pilot is referenced as secondary datum feature B at RMB.

This on the drawing

4X ⌀.125 +.004/−.001
⊕ ⌀.008 B A

A
⊥ .002 B

⌀.500±.002
B

Means this

.002 Perp tolerance

Primary RMB collapsing cylinder

The pilot is the primary datum feature B at RMB. The bottom face is referenced as secondary datum feature A and may only touch at one point.

This on the drawing

4X ⌀.125 +.004/−.001
⊕ ⌀.008 A B Ⓜ

A
⬦ .002

⌀.500±.002
⊥ ⌀.002 A
B

Means this

.002 flatness tolerance

Cylinder fixed at MMB of .504

The bottom face is referenced as primary datum feature A. The pilot is referenced as secondary datum feature B at MMB.

43

The MMB simulator for datum feature C is a **plane fixed at 66 MMB** (65 from the center of datum B plus ½ profile tolerance). Datum feature C may rotate and is free to move within the confines established by the MMB boundary. This constrains the rotation of the part.

Effect of Tertiary Datum Feature Modified at MMB

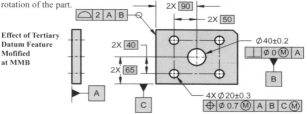

Datum feature C, modified at MMB, establishes a fixed simulator at 66 MMB to orient the DRF to the part.

The RMB simulator for datum feature C is a **plane that moves/progresses** from MMB to make maximum contact with the datum feature to constrain rotaion of the part.

Effect ofTertiary Datum Feature Modified at RMB

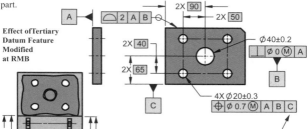

RMB simulator moves normal to make maximum contact, and level the datum feature.

Datum feature C, implied to apply at RMB, establishes a simulator that moves/progresses normal to make maximum contact with the datum feature to orient the DRF to the part.

Orientation Control at RMB With/Without Translation Modifier

The illustrations below explain the differences in establishing the DRF with a tertiary datum feature applied at RMB with and without a translation modifier according to the datum feature simulator requirements defined earlier on page 42.

Tertiary datum feature implied at RMB

Without translation modifier, datum axis B and center plane of simulator C are coincident.

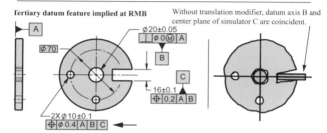

Datum feature C implied at RMB requires the simulator to expand into the slot while fixed at basic location. Since the simulator is fixed at basic and expands, it may engage a "cocked" slot to establish the DRF. This is the most common application and is usually used for key seats and location requirements.

Tertiary datum feature implied at RMB with translation modifier

With translation modifier, datum axis B and center plane of simulator C may not be coincident.

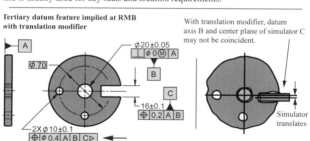

Simulator translates

Datum feature C implied at RMB requires the simulator to expand into the slot. The addition of the translation modifier does not require the simulator to be fixed at basic. It allows the simulator to translate from basic location within the position tolerance using the slot orientation to establish the DRF. This is a less common application and is usually used when the slot width is longer in length and is used for orientation.

45

Datum Targets - Pillow Block Casting

The casting has been defined on the drawing below. Manufacturing, in consultation with design, determines the manufacturing process and fixturing necessary to machine the pillow block. Manufacturing has decided to clamp the casting in a machining fixture and perform all machine operations in one set-up.

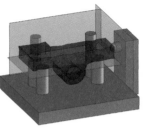

The datum targets on the drawing correspond to the datum targets on the fixture.

The datum reference frame symbol (X, Y, Z) is shown on the drawing and represents the DRF established by the datum targets.

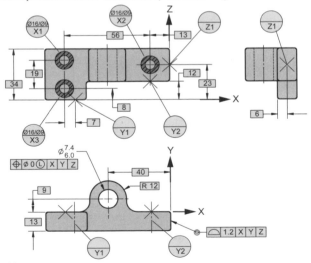

Pillow Block Machining Located to the Casting

The machined pillow block shown in the assembly to the right mounts on the bottom face, the side face and is centered in the assembly by the large hole. The pattern of three holes bolt down and fix the part in place.

The pillow block will be made from a casting, which is shown on the previous page. The machined part has an A, B, C datum reference

Pillow block assembly

frame established, and all the machined features on the part are located to this DRF. The cast part has an X, Y, Z datum reference frame and all the cast features are located to this DRF.

In order to make stock removal and resulting wall thickness calculations, the machine DRF must be located to the cast DRF. The profile and position tolerances indicated by note 2 locate the machine DRF to the cast DRF. This is what we formerly called the "first machine cut."

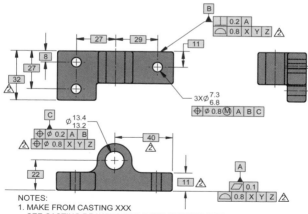

NOTES:
1. MAKE FROM CASTING XXX
   SEE CASTING DRAWING FOR DATUM TARGET INFORMATION.

⚠2 DESIGNATES THE LOCATION OF THE MACHINING TO CASTING DRF.

Movable Datum Target

The movable datum target symbol is differentiated from the datum target symbol with a triangle attached to the side. The movable datum target designates that the datum feature simulator moves to engage the part.

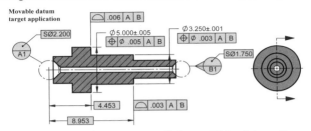

The drawing shows datum targets applied to establish a datum reference frame. Datum target A is defined as a spherical diameter of 2.200. Datum target B is defined as a spherical diameter of 1.750 and is movable.

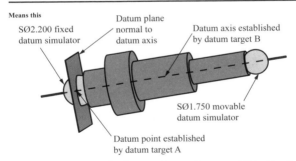

This graphic illustrates the datum reference frame established by datum targets A and B. Datum target A is a spherical simulator 2.200 in diameter and establishes a datum point and origin. Datum target B is a spherical simulator 1.750 in diameter, moves toward datum A and establishes a point. The two datum points in combination establish a DRF. All measurements originate from this DRF.

Flatness of a Surface

Flatness is the condition of a surface having all elements in one plane. A flatness tolerance specifies a tolerance zone defined by two parallel planes within which the surface must lie.

This on the drawing

Application

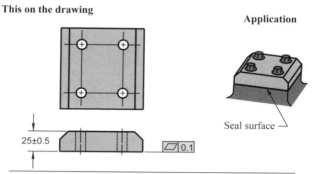

Seal surface

The surface must lie between two parallel planes 0.1 apart. In addition, the feature must be within the limits of size.

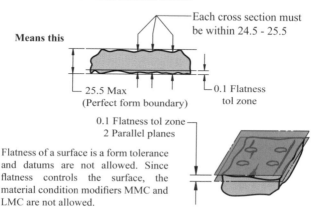

Each cross section must be within 24.5 - 25.5

25.5 Max
(Perfect form boundary)

0.1 Flatness tol zone

0.1 Flatness tol zone — 2 Parallel planes

Flatness of a surface is a form tolerance and datums are not allowed. Since flatness controls the surface, the material condition modifiers MMC and LMC are not allowed.

Flatness Verification

There are many ways to check a flatness specification, some are better than others. Just like any geometric tolerance, it depends on a lot of factors. First article or 1000th part? How are the parts produced, how many? How many parts are there to check? In process or final check? How much risk am I willing to take?

All of these factors and many more may have an effect on how the part is checked. The procedures for verification should be recorded in a dimensional measurement plan and coordinated with anyone who is involved with the part. A coordinate measuring machine (CMM) picking points can also be used to check flatness. See GeoTol Pro book.

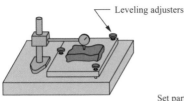

Level part using the three adjusters and move indicator over surface. The readings must not exceed flatness tolerance. Good check but time consuming.

Set part on surface plate and use feeler gage. This is a quick check used for larger tolerances. It may miss concave variations.

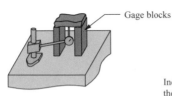

Set part upside-down on gage blocks of equal height, then indicate underneath. Not able to indicate on surface resting areas.

Indicate surface through a hole in the surface plate while sliding part. This is a good in process check. It may misread on convex parts.

Flatness of a Median Plane

This on the drawing

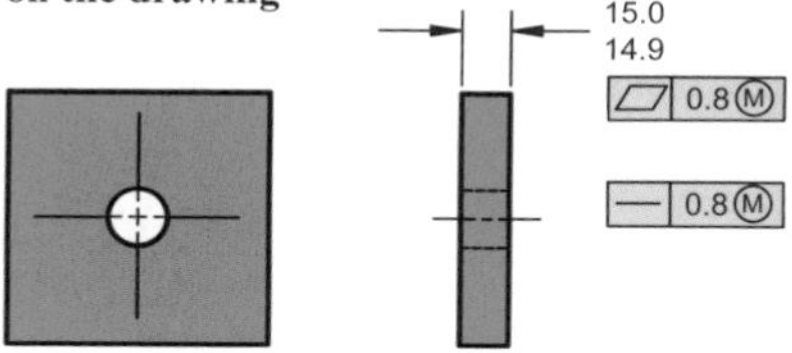
15.0
14.9
0.8Ⓜ
0.8Ⓜ

Current Practice
ASME Y14.5-2009

Past Practice
ASME Y14.5M-1994
and earlier

Application

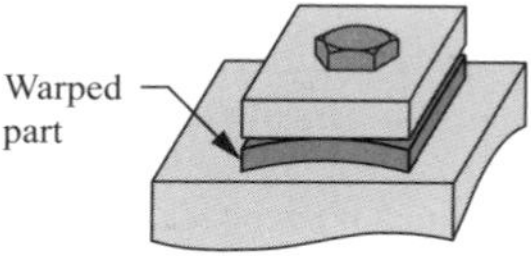
Warped
part

The local size or thickness is important, but the part may be "bowed" or warped. It will be straightened out when bolted down in the assembly.

Means this

A combination of size and the flatness tolerance requires that the entire feature must be within a virtual boundary of 15.8.

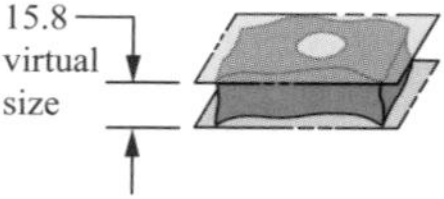
15.8
virtual
size

As the local size of the feature departs from MMC, additional flatness tolerance is allowed, equal to the departure from MMC, to a max of 0.9 flatness at LMC.

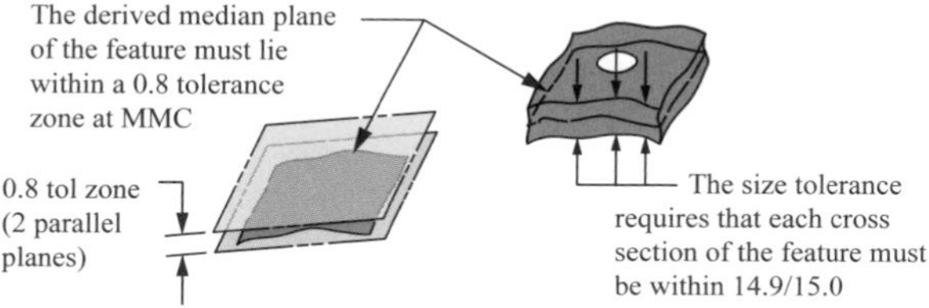
The derived median plane
of the feature must lie
within a 0.8 tolerance
zone at MMC
0.8 tol zone
(2 parallel
planes)
The size tolerance
requires that each cross
section of the feature must
be within 14.9/15.0

Straightness Line Elements on a Pin

Straightness - line elements can be applied to the surface of a pin. The specification defines a tolerance zone in which the line elements on the surface must lie. Note the feature control frame is directed to the surface to make it a surface control.

This on the drawing

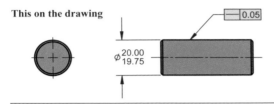

Each longitudinal element of the surface must lie between two parallel lines 0.05 apart where the two lines and the nominal axis of the part share a common plane. In addition, the feature must be within the limits of size, including perfect form at MMC. Straightness - line elements will control wasting, barrelling, and bending of the feature. It does not control taper.

Means this

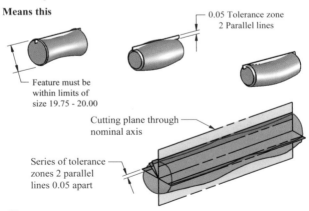

Straightness of an Axis

The straightness specification defines a tolerance zone in which the derived median line must lie. This type of control is used where the local size of the pin is important, but the pin can bend or bow beyond the perfect form at MMC requirement defined by Rule #1. Note the feature control frame is associated with the size to make it an axis control.

This on the drawing

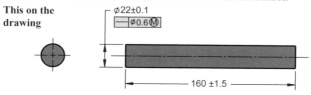

The derived median line of the feature's actual local sizes must be within a cylindrical tolerance zone of 0.6 at MMC. As the local size departs from MMC, an increase in the diameter of the tolerance cylinder is allowed equal to the amount of such departure. In addition, each circular element must be within the limits of size.

Means this

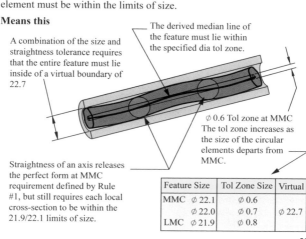

The derived median line of the feature must lie within the specified dia tol zone.

A combination of the size and straightness tolerance requires that the entire feature must lie inside of a virtual boundary of 22.7

∅ 0.6 Tol zone at MMC
The tol zone increases as the size of the circular elements departs from MMC.

Straightness of an axis releases the perfect form at MMC requirement defined by Rule #1, but still requires each local cross-section to be within the 21.9/22.1 limits of size.

Feature Size		Tol Zone Size	Virtual
MMC	∅ 22.1	∅ 0.6	
	∅ 22.0	∅ 0.7	∅ 22.7
LMC	∅ 21.9	∅ 0.8	

Circularity (Roundness)

Circularity is a condition of a surface where:

a. for a feature other than a sphere, all points of the surface intersect ed by any plane perpendicular to an axis are equidistant to that axis.

b. for a sphere, all points of the surface intersected by any plane passing through a common center are equidistant from that center.

This on the drawing

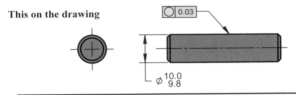

Each circular element of the surface in a plane perpendicular to the axis must lie between two concentric circles, one having a radius 0.03 larger than the other. In addition, the feature must be within the limits of size, including perfect from at MMC.

Means this

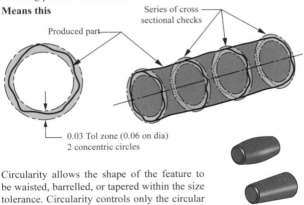

0.03 Tol zone (0.06 on dia) 2 concentric circles

Circularity allows the shape of the feature to be waisted, barrelled, or tapered within the size tolerance. Circularity controls only the circular elements of the feature.

54

Cylindricity

Cylindricity is the condition of a surface of revolution within which all points of the surface are equidistant from a common axis. The tolerance zone is two concentric cylinders within which the surface must lie.

This on the drawing

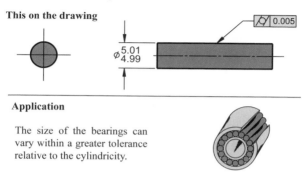

$\phi\begin{matrix} 5.01 \\ 4.99 \end{matrix}$

⌭ 0.005

Application

The size of the bearings can vary within a greater tolerance relative to the cylindricity.

The cylindrical surface of the feature must lie between two concentric cylinders, one having a radius of 0.005 larger than the other. In addition, the feature must be within the limits of size, including perfect from at MMC.

Means this

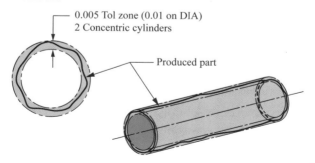

0.005 Tol zone (0.01 on DIA)
2 Concentric cylinders

Produced part

Parallelism on a Surface

This on the drawing

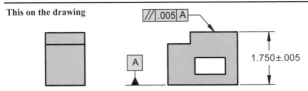

All points of the surface must lie within two parallel planes .005 apart which are parallel to datum plane A. In addition, the surface must be within the limits of size or profile.

Means this

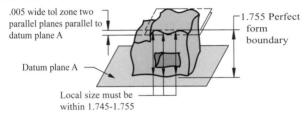

.005 wide tol zone two parallel planes parallel to datum plane A

1.755 Perfect form boundary

Datum plane A

Local size must be within 1.745-1.755

Since parallelism is a refinement is is always less than a location or size tolerance. Parallelism on a plane surface also controls the flatness. Thus, if no flatness is specified, the flatness tolerance requirement will be equal to the parallelism requirement.

Sample Inspection for Parallelism

Part is mounted on datum A and an indicator is placed on the surface. As the indicator rides on the surface, the full indicator movement (FIM) can be no more than .005. Parralelism also controls flatness.

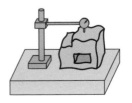

Perpendicularity on a Surface

Perpendicularity is the condition of a surface, median plane, or axis oriented at 90° to the datum reference frame.

This on the drawing

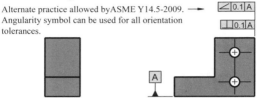

Alternate practice allowed byASME Y14.5-2009. → Angularity symbol can be used for all orientation tolerances.

The surface must lie between two parallel planes 0.1 apart. In addition, the feature must be within the applicable limits of size or location.   May have one or more datum references.

Means this

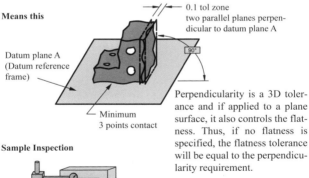

Datum plane A
(Datum reference frame)

Minimum
3 points contact

0.1 tol zone
two parallel planes perpendicular to datum plane A

90°

Perpendicularity is a 3D tolerance and if applied to a plane surface, it also controls the flatness. Thus, if no flatness is specified, the flatness tolerance will be equal to the perpendicularity requirement.

Sample Inspection

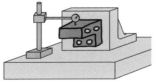

The part is mounted on datum feature A and the surface to be verified is leveled. The full indicator movement must not exceed 0.1.

Angularity on a Surface

Angularity is the condition of a surfaced, axis or center plane oriented at a specified angle to the DRF. The angularity symbol can be used for all orientation tolerances.

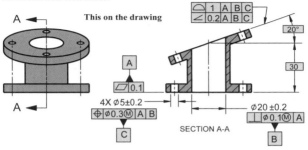

This on the drawing

SECTION A-A

Means this

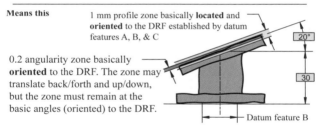

1 mm profile zone basically **located** and **oriented** to the DRF established by datum features A, B, & C

0.2 angularity zone basically **oriented** to the DRF. The zone may translate back/forth and up/down, but the zone must remain at the basic angles (oriented) to the DRF.

Datum feature B

To verify the angularity requirement, the part is mounted on datum feature A, centered on datum feature B, and oriented with datum feature C, the pattern of four holes. The part is then inclined at 20 degrees using a sine plate. The surface to be measured should now be near parallel to the surface plate. The full indicator movement on the surface should be no more than 0.2.

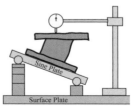

Sample Inspection

58

Perpendicularity of Zero at MMC

The two examples shown each represent a mating assembly. Example 1 specifies a .002 at MMC perpendicularity. Example 2 specifies a .000 at MMC. Notice example 2 provides a greater variation on size while still maintaining the same virtual size as example 1. The zero tolerancing at MMC or LMC may be applied to other geometric controls as well.

Example 1 - Use this method if it is necessary to control the size and orientation with separate specs.

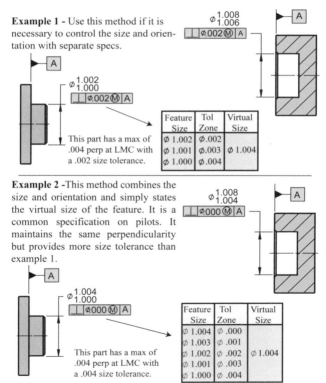

This part has a max of .004 perp at LMC with a .002 size tolerance.

Feature Size	Tol Zone	Virtual Size
∅ 1.002	∅.002	
∅ 1.001	∅.003	∅ 1.004
∅ 1.000	∅.004	

Example 2 -This method combines the size and orientation and simply states the virtual size of the feature. It is a common specification on pilots. It maintains the same perpendicularity but provides more size tolerance than example 1.

This part has a max of .004 perp at LMC with a .004 size tolerance.

Feature Size	Tol Zone	Virtual Size
∅ 1.004	∅ .000	
∅ 1.003	∅ .001	
∅ 1.002	∅ .002	∅ 1.004
∅ 1.001	∅ .003	
∅ 1.000	∅ .004	

Profile of a Surface - Bilateral Control

Profile tolerancing specifies a uniform boundary along the true profile defined by basic dimensions within which the surface must lie. Profile tolerancing can be applied on a bilateral, unilateral, or unequal distribution basis. A single arrow from the feature control frame points directly to the surface is a bilateral.

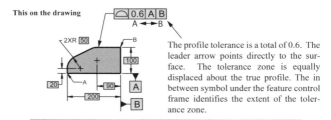

This on the drawing

The profile tolerance is a total of 0.6. The leader arrow points directly to the surface. The tolerance zone is equally displaced about the true profile. The in between symbol under the feature control frame identifies the extent of the tolerance zone.

The tolerance zone established by the profile of a surface control is three dimensional and extends along the full length and width of the considered feature. The in between symbol under the feature control frame states the tolerance extends between points A and B.

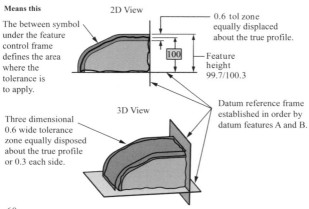

Means this

The between symbol under the feature control frame defines the area where the tolerance is to apply.

2D View

0.6 tol zone equally displaced about the true profile.

Feature height 99.7/100.3

Three dimensional 0.6 wide tolerance zone equally disposed about the true profile or 0.3 each side.

3D View

Datum reference frame established in order by datum features A and B.

Profile of a Surface - Unequal Distribution

Profile tolerance by default is a bilateral control that specifies a tolerance zone that is equally disposed about the true profile. In some cases, an unequal distribution of the tolerance zone may be desired. If an unequal distribution is required, there are two methods available to designate this specification on the drawing or model.

1. Option 1 *(New for ASME Y14.5-2009 and recommended practice)*
   The circle U symbology in the feature control frame. The value following the circle U is the amount the tolerance is displaced out adding material. The remaining amount of the total tolerance is displaced in removing material.

2. Option 2 Use two arrows on the drawing to illustrate the width and/or direction of the tolerance zone. *(Alternate earlier practice to eventually be phased out.)*

Profile Application - Unilateral Out

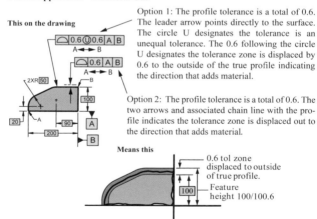

This on the drawing

Option 1: The profile tolerance is a total of 0.6. The leader arrow points directly to the surface. The circle U designates the tolerance is an unequal tolerance. The 0.6 following the circle U designates the tolerance zone is displaced by 0.6 to the outside of the true profile indicating the direction that adds material.

Option 2: The profile tolerance is a total of 0.6. The two arrows and associated chain line with the profile indicates the tolerance zone is displaced out to the direction that adds material.

Means this

0.6 tol zone displaced to outside of true profile.

Feature height 100/100.6

Profile of a Line

Profile of a line specifies a series of cross sectional uniform tolerance boundaries along the true profile, and along the full length and width of the considered feature, within which the elements of the surface must lie. Profile of a line can be applied on a bilateral, unilateral, or unequal distribution basis. It may be specified with or without a datum feature reference and applies in the view shown.

Profile of a Line - Bilateral

This on the drawing

A 0.6 total wide profile of a surface zone equally disposed about the true profile within which lies a series of 2 dimensional 0.2 wide profile of a line cross sectional tolerance zones. The surface elements of the feature must lie in the profile of a surface zone and series of refining profile of a line zones

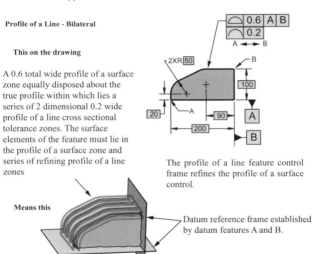

The profile of a line feature control frame refines the profile of a surface control.

Means this

Datum reference frame established by datum features A and B.

Profile of a line is often used on extruded type parts where only cross sectional zones are necessary as in use for a flexible extruded rubber moulding. Profile of a line may or may not have any datum feature references. Profile of a line applies in the view in which shown. See GeoTol Pro book for more information on controlling cutting plane direction and orientation.

Profile of a Surface - Cam Wheel Application

Profile tolerance is used to locate surfaces. It can be used to locate contoured surfaces as well as flat surfaces. The cam wheel below has two profile controls applied. The upper 0.4 profile specification is by default, a bilateral control which specifies a tolerance zone that is equally disposed about the basic true profile.

The lower 0.2 profile specification is a unequal control because of the circle U following the feature tolerance in the feature control frame. The 0 following the circle U designates the amount the tolerance zone is displaced to the outside of the basic true profile. Since zero is displaced to the outside, the profile zone is all shifted to the inside of the true profile by 0.2. The surface of the part must fall within the profile zones.

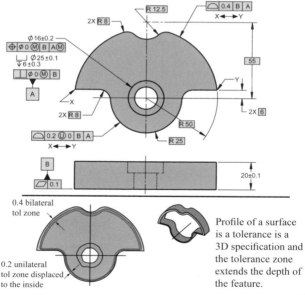

Profile of a surface is a tolerance is a 3D specification and the tolerance zone extends the depth of the feature.

Profile of a Surface - Inspection Reporting

A sample inspection report is shown for the two profile specifications. Inspection bubbles are placed next to the callouts so they may be referenced in the chart. An electronic height gage and a surface plate are used to check the two profile specifications. Four points were selected for feature 2 because of its relatively small size and large tolerance. Six points were selected for feature 1 because of its larger surface area and relatively small tolerance.

See GeoTol book for more info.

Feature	Allowed Profile	# of Pts Measured	Min/Max Deviation	Measured Profile	Accept Reject
1	.004	6	-.0005/ +.0015	.003	A
2	.010	4	+.001/ +.003	.006	A

Depending on the complexity of the measurement plan, the value of each measured point may be included in the report. When reporting, all values are converted to deviations from basic. They are reported as plus material or minus material.

The measured profile is recorded as a total zone about basic. The extreme deviation in either direction is doubled for this value. This allows it to be compared to the allowed profile.

Measured Values   Reported Values

(1)

1	.5010
2	.5002
3	.5015
4	.4998
5	.5004
6	.4995

Pt.	Deviation from Basic
1	+ .0010
2	+ .0002
3	+ .0015
4	- .0002
5	+ .0004
6	- .0005

(2)

1	1.253
2	1.252
3	1.253
4	1.251

Pt.	Deviation from Basic
1	+ .003
2	+ .002
3	+ .003
4	+ .001

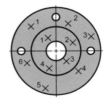

The locations of the points may also be defined. They may be shown in a simple picture or with exact x, y, z coordinates included in a chart.

Continuous Feature - Zero Tolerancing

Size tolerance applies to individual features and does not control the relationship of features. There is no relation between features unless specified. Witness lines between the features define the size of each individual feature but do not control the location between them. The location between the features may be controlled with a position tolerance or with a continuous feature symbol. This makes the group of features act like an individual feature of size.

The continuous feature symbol is used for features of size. It is not applicable to coplanar surfaces. Profile of a surface is used to control the relationship between coplanar surfaces. Continous feature is new for th ASME Y14.5-2009 standard.

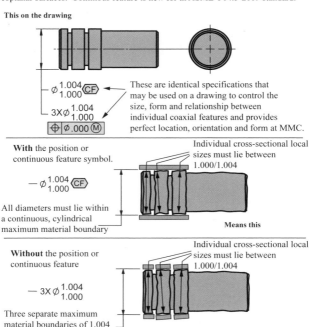

This on the drawing

ϕ 1.004 / 1.000 (CF)

3Xϕ 1.004 / 1.000

⊕ | ϕ .000 Ⓜ

These are identical specifications that may be used on a drawing to control the size, form and relationship between individual coaxial features and provides perfect location, orientation and form at MMC.

With the position or continuous feature symbol.

— ϕ 1.004 / 1.000 (CF)

All diameters must lie within a continuous, cylindrical maximum material boundary

Individual cross-sectional local sizes must lie between 1.000/1.004

Means this

Without the position or continuous feature

— 3Xϕ 1.004 / 1.000

Three separate maximum material boundaries of 1.004

Individual cross-sectional local sizes must lie between 1.000/1.004

Position tolerancing is used for locating features of size. It defines a zone within which the feature axis or center plane must lie. The size of this tolerance zone is equal to the amount of variation allowed from the true (theoretically exact) position. Basic dimensions establish the true position from the specified datums as well as the interrelationship between the features.

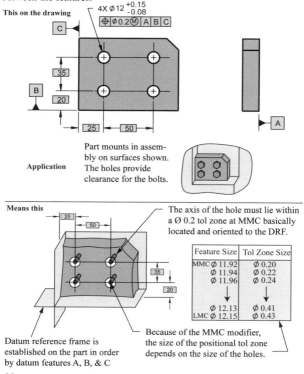

This on the drawing

$4X \varnothing 12 \begin{smallmatrix} +0.15 \\ -0.08 \end{smallmatrix}$

⊕ | ⌀0.2Ⓜ | A | B | C

C
35
B
20
25 50
A

Application Part mounts in assembly on surfaces shown. The holes provide clearance for the bolts.

Means this

25
50
35
20

The axis of the hole must lie within a ⌀ 0.2 tol zone at MMC basically located and oriented to the DRF.

Feature Size	Tol Zone Size
MMC ⌀ 11.92	⌀ 0.20
⌀ 11.94	⌀ 0.22
⌀ 11.96	⌀ 0.24
↓	↓
⌀ 12.13	⌀ 0.41
LMC ⌀ 12.15	⌀ 0.43

Datum reference frame is established on the part in order by datum features A, B, & C

Because of the MMC modifier, the size of the positional tol zone depends on the size of the holes.

Position Tolerance (continued)

The graphic below shows the sectioned imperfect part from the previous positional tolerance example. The theoretical 3D cylindrical tolerance zones control the location and orientation of the hole axes.

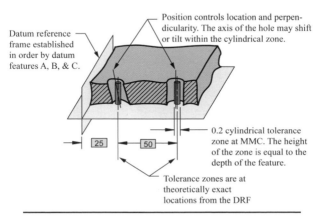

Position controls location and perpendicularity. The axis of the hole may shift or tilt within the cylindrical zone.

Datum reference frame established in order by datum features A, B, & C.

0.2 cylindrical tolerance zone at MMC. The height of the zone is equal to the depth of the feature.

25 50

Tolerance zones are at theoretically exact locations from the DRF

Functional gage for position call out

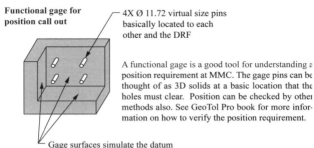

4X Ø 11.72 virtual size pins basically located to each other and the DRF

A functional gage is a good tool for understanding a position requirement at MMC. The gage pins can be thought of as 3D solids at a basic location that the holes must clear. Position can be checked by other methods also. See GeoTol Pro book for more information on how to verify the position requirement.

Gage surfaces simulate the datum reference frame established from the datum features A, B, & C.

Composite Position Tolerance

Composite position tolerancing is often used where the location of the holes to each other is important, but the location of the holes relative to the DRF is less important. The position symbol is entered once and is applicable to both horizontal segments. With composite tolerancing, the upper segment locates and orients the pattern of holes to the specified DRF. The lower segment locates the holes to each other and controls the orientation of the pattern to datum A.

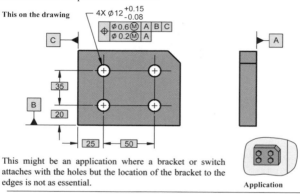

This on the drawing

This might be an application where a bracket or switch attaches with the holes but the location of the bracket to the edges is not as essential.

Application

Means this

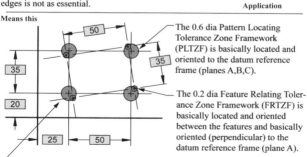

The 0.6 dia Pattern Locating Tolerance Zone Framework (PLTZF) is basically located and oriented to the datum reference frame (planes A,B,C).

The 0.2 dia Feature Relating Tolerance Zone Framework (FRTZF) is basically located and oriented between the features and basically oriented (perpendicular) to the datum reference frame (plane A).

The FRTZF may skew, rotate, and/or be displaced within the confines of the PLTZF. The axes of the holes must lie in both zones simultaneously.

The upper segment specifies the pattern location to the stated DRF.

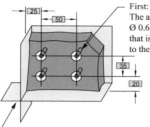

First:
The axes of the holes must lie within a Ø 0.6 at MMC pattern locating zone that is basically located and oriented to the stated datum reference frame.

4X Ø 11.32 virtual size pins basically located and oriented to each other and the DRF

Datum reference frame is established in order by datum features A, B, & C

Sample functional gage for the upper segment. The size of the holes must also be verified.

The lower segment specifies the hole to hole requirement and the orientation of this requirement to the stated DRF.

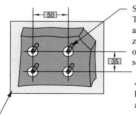

Second:
The axes of the holes must lie within a Ø 0.2 at MMC feature relating zone (hole to hole) that is only oriented (perpendicular) to the lower segment datum reference frame.

4X Ø 11.72 virtual size pins basically located to each other and perpendicular to the face

DRF is established by datum feature A. This is an orientation plane only.

Sample functional gage for the lower segment. The holes must meet both requirements.

Position Boundary

Position may be used to locate irregular features of size. to establish a maximum material boundary. In the illustration below, a datum reference frame is established by the back surface, height, and width. The profile tolerance on the irregular opening defines the size, shape, and orientation to datum A. The position tolerance defines a boundary in which no element of the feature must lie. The feature modifiers, MMC or LMC, may be applied. The word BOUNDARY is no longer required under the feature control frame for the ASME Y14.5-2009 standard.

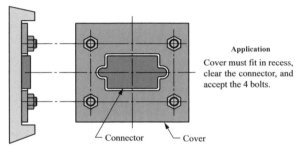

Application

Cover must fit in recess, clear the connector, and accept the 4 bolts.

Connector   Cover

This on the drawing

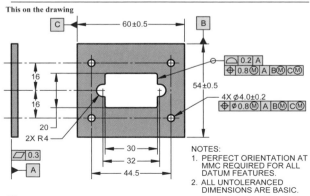

NOTES:
1. PERFECT ORIENTATION AT MMC REQUIRED FOR ALL DATUM FEATURES.
2. ALL UNTOLERANCED DIMENSIONS ARE BASIC.

70

Means this

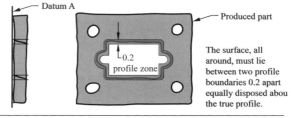

The profile requirement controls the size, shape, and orientation of the feature.

The surface, all around, must lie between two profile boundaries 0.2 apart equally disposed abou the true profile.

The position requirement locates the feature to the datum reference frame.

No portion of the surface may lie inside the virtual boundary created by the smallest profile boundary minus the position tolerance. This maximum material boundary is basically located to the datums A, B at MMB and C at MMB.

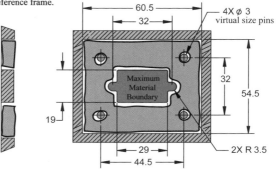

Position boundary for locating irregular features of size is a similar concept to composite profile. However, position boundary, when applied with MMC and LMC modifiers, defines only a MMB or LMB in which no part of the surface may lie. Composite profile creates both a MMB and a LMB in which the feature must lie.

Position - Multiple Controls Adding and Removing Datums

Adding and removing datums with position tolerancing allows the designer to state exacting requirements while allowing maximum manufacturing tolerance. It is sometimes easier to read these from the bottom up. The bottom callout requires the three holes to be located to each other and oriented to the face within 0.12. The next callout requires the holes to be to the face and located to the pilot within 0.25. The final callout requires the holes to be to the face, pilot and rotated to the slot within 0.85.

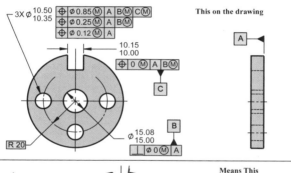

This on the drawing

View shows tolerance zones only. The holes have been omitted for clarity.

Ø 0.25 zones are basically located and oriented to the DRF established by datum features A & B. These tolerance zones are free to rotate together about the datum axis.

Means This

Ø 0.85 zones are basically located and oriented to the DRF established by datum features A, B, & C. These tolerance zones are fixed at the basic dimensions.

Ø 0.12 zones are basically located and oriented to the DRF established by datum feature A. These tolerance zones are free to move and rotate together about the datum axis.

The axes off the holes must lie in all zones simultaneously. The features also have additional tolerances as they depart from MMC.

Position Verification

As drawn

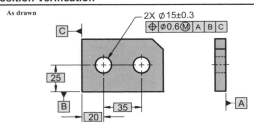

2X Ø15±0.3

⊕ | Ø0.6Ⓜ | A | B | C

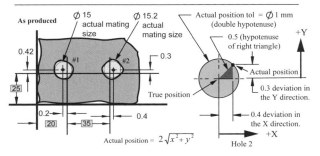

As produced

Ø 15 actual mating size

Ø 15.2 actual mating size

Actual position tol = Ø 1 mm (double hypotenuse)

0.5 (hypotenuse of right triangle)

Actual position

0.3 deviation in the Y direction.

0.4 deviation in the X direction.

True position

Actual position = $2\sqrt{x^2 + y^2}$

Hole 2

Actual position tolerance is calculated by using "X" and "Y" deviations in the position formula or position table. In order to pass inspection, the hole's actual position tolerance must be less than the allowed position.

Allowed position tolerance is calculated by taking the hole size departure from MMC and adding it to the position tolerance stated in the feature control frame.

Enter MMC of hole

Enter produced hole size

Enter "X" deviation from basic location.

Enter "Y" deviation from basic location.

Hole No.	MMC Size	Actual Size	Allowed Position	"X" Dev	"Y" Dev	Actual Position	Acc	Rej
1	14.7	15	0.9	- 0.2	0.42	0.93		X
2	14.7	15.2	1.1	0.4	0.3	1	X	

73

Circular Runout - Coaxial Features

Circular runout is a two dimensional surface to axis control. The tolerance is applied independently at each circular cross section. When applied to a surface constructed around a datum axis, circular runout controls the variations of circularity, orientation, and coaxiality.

This on the drawing

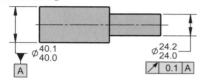

Means this

The theoretical datum feature simulator is the smallest circumscribed cylinder that contacts the high points of the feature. Depending on the accuracy required, this may be practically simulated by a collet, chuck, vee block, etc.

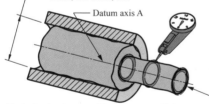

Datum axis A

Circular Runout does not control straightness or taper. Runout tolerance does not control the size and therefore the feature requires a separate size tolerance.

Each circular element of the feature must lie between two circles, one having a radius of 0.1 larger than the other, perfectly concentric to the datum axis A. Additionally, the feature must be within the limits of size (24.0/24.2), the outer boundary is 24.3. The inner boundary is 23.9.

Circular runout may be verified with a indicator, CMM, or other methods. If a dial indicator is used, the needle is placed on the surface. When the part is rotated 360 degrees about the datum axis, at each cross section the full indicator movement may be no more than 0.1. Since this is a 2D callout, the indicator is reset at each cross-section along the length of the feature.

Total Runout - Coaxial Features

Total runout is a three dimensional surface to axis control. When applied to a surface constructed around a datum axis, it controls the variations of circularity, straightness, taper, orientation, and coaxiality. The runout tolerances do not control the size and therefore the feature requires a separate size tolerance.

This on the drawing

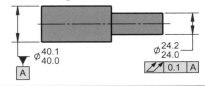

$\phi \begin{smallmatrix} 40.1 \\ 40.0 \end{smallmatrix}$

A

$\phi \begin{smallmatrix} 24.2 \\ 24.0 \end{smallmatrix}$

| ⟋⟋ | 0.1 | A |

Means this

The theoretical datum feature simulator is the smallest circumscribed cylinder that contacts the high points of the feature. Depending on the accuracy required, this may be practically simulated by a collet, chuck, vee block, etc.

Datum axis A

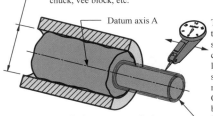

Total runout is a 3D control and requires a total sweep of the surface. This controls form, orientation, location, and taper (but not size) of the feature for a maximum of 0.1 (FIM). On this part, the outer boundary is 24.3. The inner boundary is 23.9.

The feature must lie between two cylinders, one having a radius of 0.1 larger than the other, perfectly concentric to the datum axis A. Additionally, the feature must be within the limits of size (24.0/24.2).

The total runout specification may be verified with a indicator, CMM, or other methods. If a dial indicator is used, the indicator is placed on the surface. When the part is rotated 360 degrees about the datum axis, the full indicator movement may be no more than 0.1, the indicator is also swept along the entire length of the feature parallel to the datum axis.

Runout Applied to Flat Surfaces

Both total runout and circular runout may be applied to surfaces at different angles to a datum axis. Perpendicularity and total runout provide identical results and can be used interchangeably. Circular runout controls 2D circular elements about the axis and the surface may be concave or convex within the specified size or location tolerance.

This on the drawing

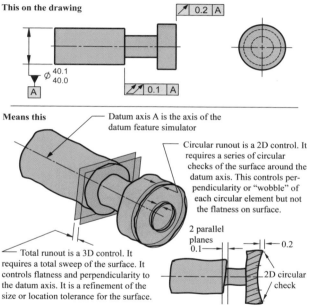

Datum axis A is the axis of the datum feature simulator

Circular runout is a 2D control. It requires a series of circular checks of the surface around the datum axis. This controls perpendicularity or "wobble" of each circular element but not the flatness on surface.

Total runout is a 3D control. It requires a total sweep of the surface. It controls flatness and perpendicularity to the datum axis. It is a refinement of the size or location tolerance for the surface.

2 parallel planes

2D circular check

Total and circular runout may be verified with a dial indicator, CMM, or other methods. If a dial indicator is used, the surface or circular elements must be within the specified runout tolerance when the part is rotated 360 degrees. Total runout requires all elements to be within the full indicator movement without a reset on the indicator. With circular runout, the indicator is reset to zero after each circular check.

Position Applied to Coaxial Features

Position for coaxial features defines a cylindrical zone within which the axis of the actual mating size of the feature must lie. Position controls orientation and location. It has no effect on size, form, or other variations in the surface. If required, the MMC or LMC modifier may be applied to the feature. MMB, LMB or RMB may be applied to the datum feature.

This on the drawing

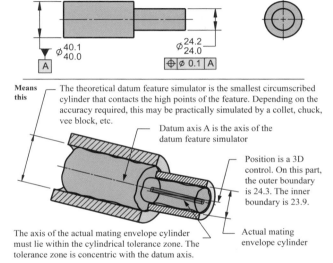

Means this The theoretical datum feature simulator is the smallest circumscribed cylinder that contacts the high points of the feature. Depending on the accuracy required, this may be practically simulated by a collet, chuck, vee block, etc.

Datum axis A is the axis of the datum feature simulator

Position is a 3D control. On this part, the outer boundary is 24.3. The inner boundary is 23.9.

The axis of the actual mating envelope cylinder must lie within the cylindrical tolerance zone. The tolerance zone is concentric with the datum axis.

Actual mating envelope cylinder

The coaxial position may be verified with a dial indicator, CMM, or other methods. If a dial indicator is used, and the Full Indicator Movement (FIM) does not exceed 0.1, the feature is good. If the FIM exceeds 0.1, the feature may still be good because as an indicator rides on the surface, it inadvertently picks up form errors (ovality). Since position is only an axis to axis control, surface variations are not included in the requirement. A mapping of the surface to exclude these form errors may be necessary to accept features beyond the 0.1 FIM.

Profile Applied to Coaxial Features

Profile of a surface for coaxial features is a 3D surface to an axis control. It defines a zone of tolerance 0.2 wide zone (each side) that is equally disposed about a basic diameter. Profile of a surface applied to the surface about the datum axis controls the variations of size, circularity, straightness, coaxiality, orientation, taper and variations in the surface.

This on the drawing

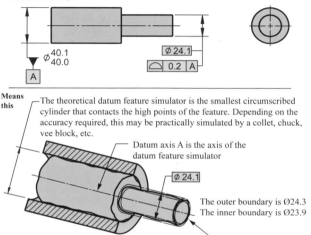

Means this

The theoretical datum feature simulator is the smallest circumscribed cylinder that contacts the high points of the feature. Depending on the accuracy required, this may be practically simulated by a collet, chuck, vee block, etc.

Datum axis A is the axis of the datum feature simulator

∅ 24.1

The outer boundary is ∅24.3
The inner boundary is ∅23.9

The feature must lie between two cylinders concentric to the datum axis A. The two cylinders are equally disposed about a basic cylinder of 24.1.

Profile of a surface specification may be verified with a dial indicator, CMM, or other methods. If a dial indicator is used, the indicator is "mastered" at the basic dimension of 12.05 (half of 24.1) from the datum axis. The entire surface must lie within the profile zone (0.2 full indicator movement) when the part is rotated 360 degrees about the datum axis. Because this is a 3D callout, the indicator is also swept along the entire length of the feature parallel to the axis.

Concentricity

Concentricity is a three dimensional control, controlling opposing median points to an axis. The application for concentricity is rare and is commonly misused. Therefore, unless there is a definite need to control the opposing median points, consider position, runout, or profile instead. Concentricity may only be applied on a RFS basis, and the datum feature reference only at RMB.

This on the drawing

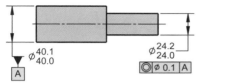

Means this

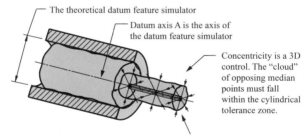

The theoretical datum feature simulator

Datum axis A is the axis of the datum feature simulator

Concentricity is a 3D control. The "cloud" of opposing median points must fall within the cylindrical tolerance zone.

The median points of all diametrically opposed elements of the feature must lie within a 0.1 cylindrical tolerance zone. This tolerance zone is concentric with the datum axis. In addition, the feature must be within the limits of size.

The concentricity specification may be verified with a dial indicator, CMM, or other methods. If a dial indicator is used, the part is mounted on the datum and two diametrically opposed, mastered indicators are placed on either side of the toleranced feature. The part is then rotated about the datum axis while watching the readings on the indicators. If they both move in or out the same it is good. If one indicator reads plus and the other reads minus, the median point is off center at that locaion. See GeoTol Pro book for more info. **www.geotol.com**

Symmetry

Symmetry is the condition where the median points of all opposed elements of a feature are congruent with the datum axis or center plane. Symmetry is the same concept as concentricity but for non cylindrical features. Symmetry differs from position in that it controls the opposing median points (derived median plane) of the surfaces, while position controls the center plane of the actual mating envelope. The application for symmetry is rare and it is commonly misused. Unless there is a definite need to control the opposing median points, consider position or profile instead.

This on the drawing

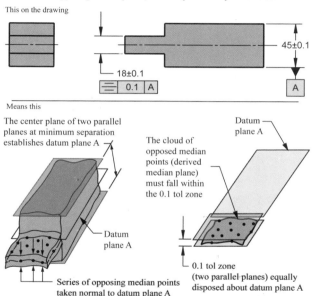

Means this

The center plane of two parallel planes at minimum separation establishes datum plane A

Datum plane A

Series of opposing median points taken normal to datum plane A

The cloud of opposed median points (derived median plane) must fall within the 0.1 tol zone

Datum plane A

0.1 tol zone (two parallel planes) equally disposed about datum plane A

The feature must be within the limits of size. In addition, all median points of opposed elements of the feature must lie within two parallel planes 0.1 apart which are equally displaced about datum plane A. The specified tolerance applies only at RFS and the datum reference can only apply on an RMB basis.